In the Night Garden...™

Annual 2012

The night is black,
And the stars are bright,
And the sea is dark and deep,
But someone I know,
Is safe and snug,
And they're drifting off to sleep.

Round and round,
A little boat,
No big   nd,
Out on
Far awa

Take the
Light the little light.
This is the way to the
Garden in the night...

Igglepiggle, iggle-onk,

we're going to catch the
Ninky Nonk!

Tombliboos
page 30

Makka Pakka
page 40

Pontipines
page 50

Look at that! Igglepiggle has found the ball! Can you colour him?

What colour is Igglepiggle's blanket?

Yes, my name is Igglepiggle
Igglepiggle–wiggle–niggle–diggle
Yes, my name is Igglepiggle
Igglepiggle–niggle–wiggle–woo!

Let's play snap!

How many matching pairs did you see? Draw a circle around the correct number.

Oh what fun!

1   2   3   4

Igglepiggle's magic blanket

Once upon a time
in the Night Garden,
Igglepiggle
came to play.

Hello, Igglepiggle.
What are you doing today?
Are you dancing in the garden?
Can we go with you?

Before he could start to skip and twirl, Igglepiggle needed to put his blanket somewhere safe.

Igglepiggle decided to hang his blanket on a tree.

That's right, Igglepiggle. Safe and sound.

Can you point to Igglepiggle's special blanket?

Igglepiggle danced all over the garden. What a funny, happy dance!

Mr and Mrs Pontipine and all their children came out of their house to watch.

Mi-mi-mi-mi-mi-mi-mi-mi-mi-mi-mi!

Who's here?
It's Makka Pakka
with his Og-pog.

Can you count ten
Pontipines peeping out
at the fun?

Oh dear. Can you guess what is going to happen?

Toot!
Toot!

Igglepiggle's
blanket is going to
fall on Makka
Pakka's head!

13

When Igglepiggle got back to the tree, his blanket had gone. Don't worry Igglepiggle. It's not far away. Look! There's your blanket.

It's walking about by itself!

The blanket was moving as if by magic.
What a surprise for Igglepiggle!
Don't worry Igglepiggle, it's only Makka Pakka.

Makka Pak...

head out and...

Now Igglepiggle ... ...anket again.

Isn't that a pip?

Lost and found

All that fun with Makka Pakka has given Igglepiggle an idea for a hiding game.

Can you see who else is taking turns to hide underneath Igglepiggle's blanket?

Use your finger to trace the letters spelling out each name.

Wottingers

Tombliboo Eee

Upsy Daisy   Haahoo

Here comes the Pinky Ponk!

When Igglepiggle rides in the Pinky Ponk, he can see all over the Night Garden. Who can he spot through the window today?

Wave hello to Igglepiggle's special friends. Now count them 1, 2, 3!

Sssssssssshh...

The Haahoos are getting ready to go to sleep in a big pillowy pile. **Look!** Here are two pictures of the friends saying goodnight.

Are the Haahoo pictures exactly the same? Try and find two differences between the top and the bottom one.

Haa-hooooo!

Pip-pip, onk-onk!

19

Upsy Daisy loves to sing!

Upsy Daisy! Here I come,
I'm the only Upsy one!
I'm the only Daisy too!
Ipsy Upsy Daisy doo!

Upsy Daisy is a very happy dolly today! Draw yourself dancing next to her. Now colour the picture.

Circle the special object that makes Upsy Daisy's singing ring across the garden.

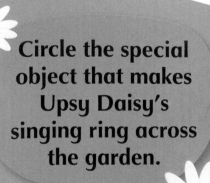

Dizzy daisy patch

Upsy Daisy's bed has run away again!
Can you help her find it?

Make your fingers skip round and round the daisy patch, all the way back to the bed.

Oooh! Daisy Doo!

Colour this flower when you finish.

Upsy Daisy kisses everything!

Once upon a time in the Night Garden, Upsy Daisy came to play.

Daisy Doo!

Can you guess what Upsy Daisy is doing?

Mwah! Mwah!

That's right! Upsy Daisy loves the garden so much, she has decided to kiss everything in it.

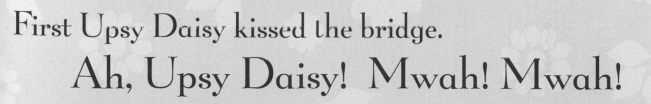

First Upsy Daisy kissed the bridge.
Ah, Upsy Daisy! Mwah! Mwah!

Ping!
Something magical happened.
The lights on the bridge twinkled and
lovely music started to play.

What a happy bridge.

Next Upsy Daisy kissed a flower.
Ah Upsy Daisy!
Mwah! Mwah!

The flower grew and grew until...
Ping! Lots of pretty petals
sparkled in the sunshine.

Ping!

Ping!

Upsy Daisy kissed a tree.
Ah Upsy Daisy!
Mwah! Mwah!

Ping! Beautiful blossoms
burst from the branches.

What a happy flower.
What a happy tree.

24 **Colour Upsy Daisy's pretty flower.**

What do you think Upsy Daisy wanted to kiss after that?

Oooh! Oh Upsy Daisy!

She wanted to kiss her bed! Upsy Daisy's bed is her favourite thing.

Oooh! Oooh! Oooh!

Upsy Daisy chased the bed all around the garden, but it would not stop

25

Hello, Upsy Daisy!
Oh! Upsy Daisy!

Igglepiggle thought his friend looked a little sad.
Poor Upsy Daisy.

Igglepiggle decided to cheer up
Upsy Daisy with a happy dance.

I wonder who Upsy Daisy wants
to kiss now?

Upsy Daisy clapped her hands
then ran up to Igglepiggle.

Ah Upsy Daisy!
   Mwah! Mwah!

Upsy Daisy kissed Igglepiggle.
Mwah! Mwah!

So Igglepiggle kissed U

                    Wh   Daisy!

Isn't that a pip?

Best friends

Now that you've heard Upsy Daisy's kissing story, would you like to tell it to a friend?

One day  felt so happy, she decided to kiss everything in the garden.  kissed the brid  and a tree. Next  decided to kiss her  .  chased her up and down, but it wouldn't stop for a kiss! So  kissed

When you see these pictures say the right words.

Igglepiggle   Upsy Daisy   bed

instead. Now   and   are

very happy. Isn't that a pip?

29

The Tombliboos take a tumble!

Ombliboo Tombliboo,
knock on the door.
Ombliboo Tombliboo,
sit on the floor.

Ombliboo Tombliboo,
here is my nose.
Ombliboo Tombliboo,
that's how it goes!

1   2   3

4   5

One, two, three tumbly Tombliboos! Can you colour the spotty trousers on their washing line? The number key will help you choose the right crayons to use.

30

All aboard the Ninky Nonk!

Tombliboo Ooo, Unn and Eee want to ride the Ninky Nonk today! Which carriage should they take?

Draw a line from the Tombliboos to their special carriage.

Now wave goodbye to the Ninky Nonk.

High 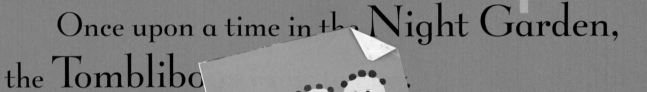 and low

Once upon a time in the Night Garden,
the Tombliboos

Hello, Tombliboo Tombliboo Ooo.
Hello, Tombliboo

Pop! Pop! Pop!
One by one, the
Tombliboos
squeezed through
the tiny opening
into their home.

Tombliboo Ooo

Tombliboo Eee

Tombliboooooo!

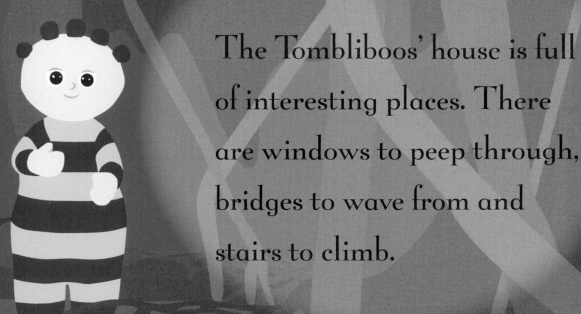

The Tombliboos' house is full of interesting places. There are windows to peep through, bridges to wave from and stairs to climb.

First Tombliboo O climbed up high. Then Tombli climbed up too. And what did Tombliboo Unn do?

That's right, Tombliboo Unn. You climbed the highest of all!

The Tombliboos' climbing game was lots of fun.

Tombliboo Tombliboo-oooooo!

The Tombliboos high, high, took turns climbing high, right to the top of their house.

1 2 3

Parp!
Parp!

Who's
here?

Ikka akka ooo!

It's Makka Pakka!

The Tombliboos popped their heads out of the tiny opening of their home. **One, two, three!**

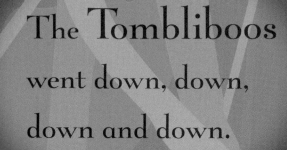

The Tombliboos went down, down, down and down.

Tombliboooooo! Tomblibooooooo!

Lower, and lower, and lower and lower... all the way to the bottom of their house.

Out come the Tombliboos!

Pop! Pop! Pop!

Can you colour Makka Pakka's soap and sponge?

36

Makka Pakka took his sponge and soap from the Og-pog.

Tombliboo Unn, Tombliboo Ooo and Tombliboo Eee waited in a line.

What was Makka Pakka going to do?

Yes! The Tombliboos went lower and lower, all the way down to have their faces washed.

Isn't that a pip?

I spy someone high!

The Tombliboos have climbed high, high, high again, all the way up to the top of their house. Look across the garden, then help them decide who is high and who is low?

Who is the highest?

Who is the lowest?

What whizzes along, down on the ground?

Is Makka Pakka in or out?

Who is higher?
The Pontipines
or Igglepiggle?

Makka Pakka
loves his
Og-pog!

Makka Pakka loves pushing his Og-pog round the garden, collecting stones for all his friends. Draw round the dots, then colour Makka Pakka.

How many stones can you count?

Makka Pakka
Akka wakka
Mikka makka moo!

Makka Pakka
Appa yakka
Ikka akka ooo!

Hum dum
Agga pang
Ing ang ooo!

Makka Pakka
Akka wakka
Mikka makka moo!

40

Who's on the Trubliphone?

Ting! Ting! Makka Pakka's calling someone on the Trubliphone. Could it be you?

Makka Pakka!

Draw a picture of yourself talking to Makka Pakka. Don't forget to put a bright red Trubliphone in your hand!

The **very** bouncy ball!

Once upon a time in the Night Garden, Makka Pakka came to play.

Makka Pakka was getting his Og-pog ready... when the ball bounced by!

The ball bounced up and down, up and down, past Makka Pakka and his Og-pog. It bounced all the way to the Pontipines' house.

What fun!

Makka Pakka!

Look, Makka Pakka – stones!

Can you guess what he did next?

Makka Pakka washed the stones with his sponge.

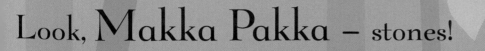

Then Makka Pakka dried the stones with his Uff-uff.

One... two... three... four... five clean, dry stones.

**Can you count five stones?
Which stone do you like the best?**

The Pontipines knocked the ball high into the air, then came to see what Makka Pakka was doing.

Hello, Makka Pakka!
Hello, Pontipines!

Makka Pakka was carefully stacking the stones, one on top of the other.

Makka Pakka
Ing ang ooo!

One...
two...
three...
four...
five
stones
in a pile!

44

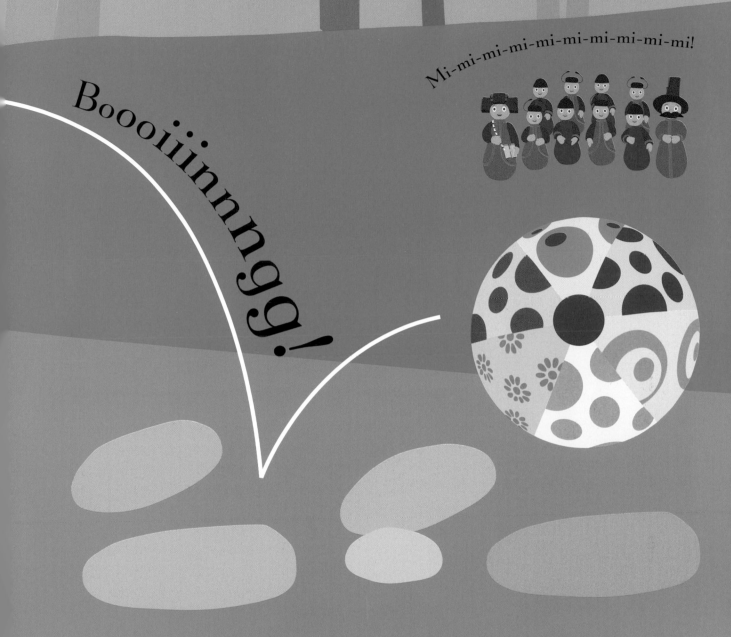

Mi-mi-mi-mi-mi-mi-mi-mi-mi-mi!

Boooiiinngg!

Oh dear. Look at what the ball did.
Makka Pakka's pile of stones got knocked down!

Time to build them up again Makka Pakka.
One... two... three... four... five.

That's better.

Oooh! Makka Pakka!

Oops! What's

The ball has knocked down

Makka Pakka! Poor Makka Pakka.

What did Makka Pakka
do when the ball had bounced away?

He stood back up again!

That's right, Makka Pakka,
up you get! Safe and sound.

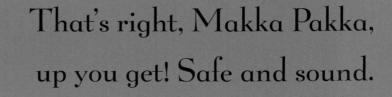

Pip-pip,
onk-onk!

The ball loves Makka Pakka.
And Makka Pakka loves
the ball.

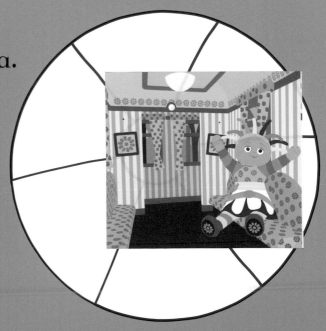

Isn't that a pip?

**Colour the ball in
your favourite colours.**

Mikka makka moo!

Funny favourites

Makka Pakka has so many favourite things he can't choose between them. He loves the ball, his Og-pog and his trumpet too!

Can you help Makka Pakka's friends find their favourite things? Draw a line to match each one up with their favourite object.

The favourite things all begin with the same sound. What is it? Use your finger to trace round the shape.

What is your favourite thing? Draw a picture of it here.

49

The Pontipines
go into the garden!

The Pontipines are friends of mine,
Although they're only small –
And even when there's ten of them,
They're hardly there at all!

Ten teeny tiny
Pontipines!
Count up every one.

1 2 3
4 5 6 7
8 9 10

50

Here's a house!

The Pontipines live next door to the Wottingers. Mr and Mrs Wottinger have four Wottinger boys and four Wottinger girls. They always wave hello when they see each other!

Wave to the Wottingers!

Where are the Wottinger family today?
Colour in a leaf for everyone that you find.

1 2 3 4 5 6 7 8 9 10

Mr Pontipine's music to play

Once upon a time
in the Night Garden,
the Pontipines
came to play.

Ten little Pontipines
all in a row, altogether
off they go.

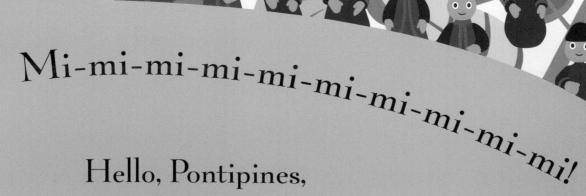

Mi-mi-mi-mi-mi-mi-mi-mi-mi-mi!

Hello, Pontipines,
what are you doing today?

52

The Pontipines were eating their dinner outside in the garden.

Oh dear! Mr Pontipine's moustache flew off.

Mr Pontipine can't eat his dinner without his moustache.

Whheeeeeee!

Where did **Mr Pontipine**'s moustache go?

The **moustache** got stuck on the **chimney!**

Whheeeeeee!

Off it goes again. Poor **Mr Pontipine.**

The Pontipines chased the moustache all around the garden.

Look at that! Mr Pontipine's moustache is stuck to the gazebo.

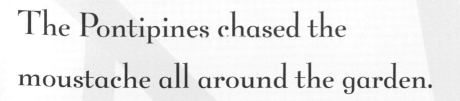eee!

Off it ~~went~~ Mr Pontipine.

Next the ~~moustache~~ got stuck on the bridge.

Mi-mi-mi-mi-mi-mi-mi-mi-mi-mi!

Follow the moustache all around the garden.

The Pontipines climbed aboard
the Ninky Nonk to try and
catch Mr Pontipine's moustache.

Off it goes again.

Poor Mr Pontipine.

Whheeeeeeee!

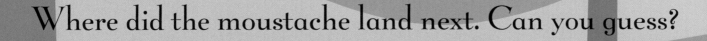

Where did the moustache land next. Can you guess?

Yes! It got stuck on the Pinky Ponk.

But look, Pontipines! Here it comes!

Oops! Now the moustache is stuck to Mrs Pontipine!

Mrs Pontipine gave the moustache back to Mr Pontipine. Thank you, Mrs Pontipine!

Isn't that a pip?

57

Mi-mi-mi-mi-mi moustaches!

Where do you think Mr Pontipine's moustache looks the funniest? Draw round the moustache shape with a pencil when you have decided.

Find something blue in the picture.

Count three tumbly Tombliboos.

Mr Pontipine's moustache ends up in all sorts of funny places. Where has it flown to today?

Point to Upsy Daisy's smiling face.

59

Time to go to sleep everybody

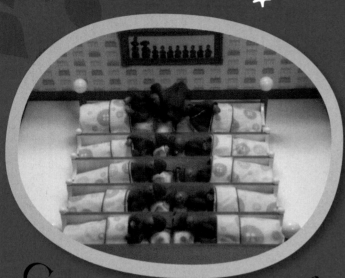

Go to sleep, Pontipines.

Use your fingers to tiptoe around the garden, saying goodnight to your friends. Can you sing a little lullaby to give them all sweet dreams?

Go to sleep, Tombliboos.

Go to sleep, Upsy Daisy.

Go to sleep, Makka Pakka.